Night Combat

Stephen Rickard

Rans☂m

It is night.

They are marching at night.

Ransom Neutron Stars
Night Combat
by Stephen Rickard

Published by Ransom Publishing Ltd.
Unit 7, Brocklands Farm, West Meon, Hampshire GU32 1JN, UK
www.ransom.co.uk

ISBN   978 178591 427 0
First published in 2017
Reprinted 2018

There is a reading comprehension quiz available for this book in the popular
Accelerated Reader® software system. For information about ATOS, Accelerated
Reader, quiz points and reading levels please visit www.renaissance.com. Accelerated
Reader, AR, the Accelerated Reader Logo, and ATOS are trademarks of Renaissance
Learning, Inc. and its subsidiaries, registered common law or applied for in the U.S.
and other countries. Used under license.

The right of Stephen Rickard to be identified as the author of this Work has been
asserted by him in accordance with sections 77 and 78 of the Copyright, Design and
Patents Act 1988.

They are looking for . . .
them.

If they see **them**, they might
need to fight them.

This is the job that they do.

They march on the road.

The moon is high.

They check up and down
the road.

They need to keep the road
secure.

If they need to fight,
they will fight.

This is the job that they do.

It all seems OK.

They wait a bit, then they march on.

A cat runs in the road.

They see it in the torch light.

The cat turns and looks
at them. It feels no fear.

Then it runs off.

They turn and march on,
up the road.

In the moonlight they can see
a wooden shed, far off
up the road.

Is it **them**?

They march on,
up to the shed.

It is all they can do.

They cannot go back.

They look at the shed
as they march up to it.

They need to maintain sharp
wits.

They get to the shed.

They rush up to it.

They need to be sure that
they are not in the shed.

In the light of a torch,
they look into the shed.

It is a mess.

They see a chair, a hammer
and a pair of boots.

They cannot see guns
or shells.

Is this just a farm hut?

They cannot be sure.

They march on.

It is all they can do.

For this is the job
that they do.

Now they need to check
the woods.

They might be in the woods.

They run to the woods.

Will they see combat tonight?

Now the night turns black.

Now there is no light
from the moon.

Soon it will rain.

In the dark of night
it is hard to see.

They have sharp ears now.

They can hear an owl hoot.
It is far off in the trees.

They cannot hear **them**,
but they can see a shadow
in the night.

Is the shadow **them**?

Will they see combat tonight?

They march on.

They see the shadow.

No, it is OK. It is just a kid.

They need to keep hush.

If they meet **them**, they will be in a fix.

Now they feel rain
and they all get wet.

The rain turns to hail
and the road turns to mud.

This is not good.
This is not fun!

They all feel a chill,
but this is the job they do.

They march on.

Soon it will be light.

Soon the sun will be up.

With a sigh, they all march on.

Tonight was hard, but it was good that they did not see combat.

For this is the job they do.

Ransom Neutron Stars

Night Combat
Word count **453**

Covers:
Letters and Sounds Phase 3

Phonics

Phonics 1	Not Pop, Not Rock Go to the Laptop Man Gus and the Tin of Ham	*Phonics 2*	Deep in the Dark Woods **Night Combat** Ben's Jerk Chicken Van
Phonics 3	GBH Steel Pan Traffic Jam Platform 7	*Phonics 4*	The Rock Show Gaps in the Brain New Kinds of Energy

Book bands

Pink	Curry! Free Runners My Toys	*Red*	Shopping with Zombies Into the Scanner Planting My Garden
Yellow	Fit for Love The Lottery Ticket In the Stars	*Blue*	Awesome ATAs Wolves The Giant Jigsaw
Green	Fly, May FLY! How to Start Your Own Crazy Cult The Care Home	*Orange*	Text Me The Last Soldier Best Friends